Books to the ceiling,
Books to the sky.
My pile of books
Is a mile high.
How I love them!
How I need them!
I'll have a long beard
By the time I read them.

—Arnold Lobel

This publication made possible by the Half Price Books Community Services Corporation. For more information about this project, or any of our other literacy endeavors, visit our web site at www.halfpricebooks.com.

Half Price Books Environmental Philosophy

A healthy environment, locally and globally, is vital to our business. We view protection of the environment as a journey, not a destination. We began that journey more than 35 years ago and it continues today. Each employee of Half Price Books and its subsidiaries has responsibility for stewardship of our natural resources and must strive to conduct business in ways that protect and preserve the environment. Our employees, business partners, suppliers and consumers must all work together to continuously find innovative ways to foster the efficient use of natural resources, prevention of waste and sound management of paper, energy and water. Doing so not only benefits the environment, it makes good business sense. Because of our environmental commitment, Half Price Books has chosen New Leaf paper for the printing of this book.

NEW LEAF PAPER®

ENVIRONMENTAL BENEFITS STATEMENT
of using post-consumer waste fiber vs. virgin fiber

Half Price Books saved the following resources by using New Leaf Reincarnation Matte, manufactured with electricity that is offset with Green-e® certified renewable energy certificates, 100% recycled fiber and 50% post-consumer waste, and processed chlorine free.

trees	water	energy	solid waste	greenhouse gases
51 fully grown	11,138 gallons	23 million Btu	2,437 pounds	4,118 pounds

Calculations based on research by Environmental Defense and other members of the Paper Task Force.

©2007 New Leaf Paper   www.newleafpaper.com

ANCIENT FOREST FRIENDLY™   Green-e   NEW LEAF PAPER manufactured with wind power

SAY GOOD NIGHT TO ILLITERACY

13TH EDITION

Half Price Books would like to dedicate this book
to all adults learning to read for their children,
all the children learning to read for their future and all the aspiring
writers who find solace in the written word.

About This Book

Half Price Books has been supporting
literacy since its founding in 1972.
We sponsored our first Bedtime Storybook
Contest, open to writers of all ages, in 1994.
Through the years we have received
entries from some of the most talented,
undiscovered writers in the country.
Each year the Bedtime Storybook Contest
is greeted with great enthusiasm. We appreciate
our customers' continued support of this contest,
and would like to thank the writers, illustrators
and judges for their time and dedication.

TABLE OF CONTENTS

Missing the Big Parade 6

Harvey & the Horrible Sneeze 8

Frequent Flyer 10

Snowflakes In the Night 12

When I Grow Up 14

Grandpa Pete and Me 16

Seasons of Fun 18

The Adventures of a Housecat 20

My Adventures 22

Isabelle Winkle Touches the Moon 24

Animal Coat Catastrophe 26

Ask Yourself a Question 28

The Box 30

Ladybug 32

Walking the Dog 34

Grandpa's Favorite Place 36

It Didn't Stop There 38

Sleepy Head 40

Little Green Tree Frogs 42

Achoo! In the Deep Blue 44

Missing the Big Parade

The big parade is starting.
Sunny's heart pounds with the beat.
BOOM-BOOM it goes, but not for the show
Making its way down the street.

She wanders behind the crowd
That stands three deep along Main.
She finds the perfect viewing spot,
A comfy seat in shady terrain.

"You'll miss the whole parade!"
Brother says, thinking he's so smart.
But as the crowd is cheering loud,
Sunny waits for her show to start.

She sees a man with ice cream cones.
He swats at two bothersome bees.
A small girl tilts her head WAY back
And lets out an elephant sneeze.
ACHOO!

Two startled look-a-like brothers
Let go of their matching balloons.
A monkey races after the strings
As his owner grinds lofty tunes.

An old man pushes a cart.
He joins the jolly affair,
And soon the smell of popcorn
Sweetly a-salts the air.

A quarter rolls along the street.
Its owner moves his nimble feet.

He wears one shoe and holds the other
As he runs—FLIP FLOP—away from Mother.

A clown hands out kazoos to blow,
And big, loud kids put on a show.

On the corner—CRASH! They meet.
Kids and clown and chasing feet.

HOORAY!
Sunny claps and cheers
At the crazy, mixed-up mess.
With a grin, she gets to her feet
And smoothes her wrinkled dress.

"I don't get it," Brother says.
"You missed the whole sha-bang!"
"No," says Sunny, standing tall.
"I didn't miss a thing."

—Carmella Van Vleet

Illustrated by Roman Koeller

Harvey and the Horrible Sneeze

Harvey Herkimer Snirkfoozle
Woke one morning needing to sneeze.
This sneeze was a doozle.
It felt like his nose was full of bees!
"Ahhh…,"said Harvey.
He said it again.
He was all ready to sneeze,
But then—
To his dismay,
The sneeze went away.
Harvey had no choice
But to get ready for the day.
The feeling came back
When Harvey walked to school.
His eyes got all teary,
His mouth began to drool.

Ahhh…,"said Harvey.
He said it again.
He was all ready to sneeze,
But then—
To his dismay,
The sneeze went away.
Harvey had no choice
But to continue on his way.
The feeling came back
When Harvey was in class.
His nose started to wiggle.
He hoped the feeling would pass.
Ahhh…,"said Harvey.
He said it again.
He was all ready to sneeze,
And then—
His eyes began to water.
His nostrils began to flare.
"Ahh," he said again louder
And leapt up from his chair.

"Achoo!" sneezed out Harvey.
"Achoo!" he sneezed once more.
"Achoo!" he sneezed a third time.
"Achoo!"sneezed sneeze number four.
Harvey sighed.
He opened his eyes.
He looked around the room.
He gasped in surprise.
Where once there were walls,
There was only a floor.
The windows were gone,
So was the door.
"Class dismissed," said his teacer
With her hands on her head.
"Go home, Harvey.
Go home. Go to bed."
So, when you feel that tingling
From you nose to your knees,
Think of Harvey Herkimer Snirkfoozle
And his horrible, horrible sneeze.

—Amy Nichols

9

Illustrated by Halley Palmer

FREQUENT FLYER

My plane had a bug in the seat next to me.
I inquired, "How come you are here?"
With wiggly antennae, the bug blurted out,
"There are no empty seats in the rear."

Astonished, I answered, "You're on an aircraft.
This is such an odd place for a bug.
Shouldn't you be in the grass, on a tree,
Or at my house under a rug?

"Bugs, as a rule, do not take off in planes.
They buzz around streetlights, no higher.
Most airlines I know don't assign bug-size seats,
Or have programs called, 'Bug Frequent Flyer.'

"Now, I have heard of bugs that infect a PC,
Or attach to an eavesdropping phone.
But I've never imagined one high in the sky,
Talking and traveling alone."

The bug seemed offended. He spread out his wings.
I wasn't the seatmate he'd planned.
And through his antennae, I caught what he said,
"I'll be sure to take off when we land."

—Margaret King

Snowflakes in the Night

The winter sky turns black to gray.
Night freezes in mid-air.
I step outside and—whoosh!—the wind
Blows diamonds through my hair.

My nightgown is a princess dress.
I wear a crown of white.
I rule a fairy kingdom made
Of snowflakes in the night.

The garden sentry bids me down
A powdered sugar lane.
He wags his tail to tell that all
Is well in my domain.

Beneath the lamppost, fairies twirl.
Their dance bejewels the sky.
They pirouette and curtsy to
Their princes passing by.

Tall pines reach with frosted limbs
To dust the stars and moon.
Who's that dangling from a bough?
The court jester raccoon.

A royal sparrow mines for jewels,
Too busy now to sing.
With skill, she pecks and polishes
A ruby for my ring.

Thistles tumble from their beds
To skate across the ice.
A blast of stardust—Poof! —they turn
To troops of silver mice.

The fairies drift off one by one;
Their ballroom now is still.
They spread a blanket on the ground
And sleep through evening's chill.

Softly in the distance calls
A voice I've heard before.
I follow sparking footprints to
The castle's open door.

High atop the roof, my dragon
Dreams of fiery tricks.
With every snore a curl of smoke
Escapes her throat of bricks.

Icicle lanterns shimmer 'round
My goodnight-kissing queen.
At last inside, I melt in
Sleepy robes of velveteen.

The king escorts me to my room,
Aglow in pale moonlight.
Enthroned in quilts of down I dream
Of snowflakes in the night.

—Janna Matthies

Illustrated by Ingrid Sundberg

When I Grow Up

"When I grow up, I want to be a pirate!" I yelled to my parents.
"I'll walk around on a great big ship singing songs about the sea and
 have a parrot for a pet."

"What if you get tired of being at sea?" my father asked me.

"Then, I'll go on land and be a farmer," I replied. "I'll work from sunrise to
 sunset, watching my plants grow until they're taller than I am."

"What if you get tired of farming?" asked my mother.

"Then, I'll become an astronaut," I replied. "I'll get to fly around in space
 and find new life on other planets."

"What if you miss earth?" my father asked.

"Then, I will become a judge," I answered.
"I'll get a big white wig and wear black robes."

"And what if you get tired of wearing a wig and robes?" my mother asked me.

"Then, I'll be an explorer," I responded. "I'll go all over the world looking for lost tribes and forgotten places."

"What if you don't want to travel anymore?" asked my father.

"Then, I shall become a doctor," I answered. "I'll make everyone feel better."

"What if you don't want to be a doctor anymore?" my mother asked.

"Then I will become a monk," I replied. "I will live quietly in the mountains with other monks."

"What if you miss your family?" my father asked.

"Then, I will return home."

"That would be nice," my mother smiled.

"But for now," I said, "I've decided to just be a child."

—Savannah Lyons

16

Illustrated by Erla Shehu

GRANDPA PETE AND ME

It's Grandpa Pete and me again,
All snug in grandpa's chair.
We've settled in to read our book,
We're quite a cozy pair.

Our bookmark points to chapter two,
We're back in Wonderland.
(You folks who do not like to read
Just wouldn't understand.)

We've tumbled down the rabbit's hole,
Saw Alice eat some cake.
I'm loving chapter two.
(I hear she cries a salty lake.)

But, sadly, I must stop.
(And just as Alice starts to weep!)
I power down my laptop.
Grandpa Pete is fast asleep.

— Donna Lee Murphy

Seasons of Fun

In the summer, seeds with wings,
Helicopters, whirling 'round.
Spinning, whizzing, try to catch them,
Fast before they hit the ground.

In autumn, leaves turn many colors
And fall from trees, floating down.
Walk along the crunchy carpet,
Red, brown, yellow. What a sound!

In the winter, falling softly,
Twirling, dancing on cold breeze.
Gather snowflakes, roll and shape
A snow-friend who won't mind the freeze.

In the springtime, dropping, plopping,
Raindrops sparkle, pitter-patter.
Search for rainbows, watch for worms,
Look for puddles, splash and splatter.

So many presents come from the sky.
In every weather, there's a reason
To go outside, have some fun and
Celebrate each delightful season.

— Cynthia M. Peebles

Illustrated by Veronica Hebard

19

Adventures of a Housecat

I have no trees to scale and climb.
The shelves in the living room do just fine.

I leap from the TV top to the coffee table.
I'm glad my legs are strong and able.

I make my way to get a drink,
Which I get from the pond in the kitchen sink.

My den lies underneath the bed,
Which is my favorite place to lay my head.

A pen cap serves as my entertainment.
I have played with almost anything, you name it.

I nap all day and play all night.
I like it best to give my owner a fright.

I've never encountered any other creatures
Except for my owner's dirty sneakers.

I have not tasted any mice.
My chicken flavored cat food is just as nice.

I've never been outside, you see,
The life of a housecat is fine with me.

—Jessica Van Roekel

Illustrated by Aleks Hadden

21

MY ADVENTURES

I met three little pigs,
Helped them build a house.
I've shared milk and cookies
With a little mouse.
Once I sailed with pirates
Through the seven seas.
I've flown through the sky
Dodging clouds with ease.
I've ridden on a dragon
In the setting sun,

Been inside a castle,
Had a lot of fun.
I've found a secret garden
Filled with tasty berries.
I've talked to elves and gnomes,
Danced with pretty fairies.
But on all of my adventures,
Wherever they may be,
My nose is in a book.
That's a guarantee.

— Alex Rudd

Illustrated by Chris Goodwin

ISABELLE WINKLE TOUCHES THE MOON

Isabelle Winkle loves to swing. She could spend the entire day on her swing, going higher and higher. "I wonder how far I can go," Isabelle thought one day. "I'll bet I can reach the tops of the trees."

She leaned back in her swing, ready to take off. Isabelle swung up and up, swishing past the dandelions, going higher and higher until her toes brushed the leaves on the tree. With a burst of energy, Isabelle flew up into the branches, startling three baby bluebirds in a nest. She swung back down and peered up through the leaves.

"I'll bet if I try harder, I can reach the top of my house." So Isabelle pumped her legs, back and forth, faster and faster. Before she knew it, she'd soared past the leaves, past the tops of the trees, and tapped her foot on the chimney.

"That wasn't' so far at all." She paused back down on the ground, catching her breath. "I know if I try even harder than before, I can reach the clouds in the sky!" Isabelle held tight to the swing. She swung past the leaves, past the tops of the trees, past the chimney on the top of her house, until she popped right through a cloud and into a flock of ducks.

"Coming through!" shouted Isabelle, her foot barely missing a flapping wing. "I'm not stopping here!"

Isabelle gathered all the strength in her body and lifted off for a great journey on her swing.

Higher and higher she rose, her legs a blur as she zoomed past the leaves, past the tops of the trees, past the chimney on top of her house and past the clouds in the sky.

24

Illustrated by Katie Beckman

"I'm an astronaut!" Isabelle exclaimed as she launched up and up and up and up...until she stretched her legs out as far as they'd go and ever so lightly touched the moon. Isabelle Winkle laughed and grabbed moon dust with her toes. She gazed back through the stars to see how far she'd gone. The earth looked like a tiny marble in a deep, dark sky.

Isabelle's stomach grumbled and she remembered it was almost suppertime. She pushed off the moon and slowly drifted back down to her very own yard, in her very own swing. As soon as Isabelle's feet touched the ground, her mother peeked her head outside. "There you are!" she called from the door. "I've been looking for you. Where did you go, to the moon and back?"

Isabelle just smiled and wiggled her toes.

—Katie Beckman

25

ANIMAL COAT CATASTROPHE

The animals were excited. Creator had called them to the campfire. It was time to distribute coats. All the animals pushed into a crowd—all except Zebra. Since the animals were created in alphabetical order, Zebra knew he would be last to get a coat. He decided to eat, while everyone else was gone, and he could get the best pickings.

Soon Armadillo strutted by, proud of his gleaming gray armor. With his chin held high, he stumbled over a rock and crashed into the ground. Zebra laughed as Armadillo shuffled away in his now cracked coat. Later, Kudu bounded by with long, gleaming horns. When Zebra complimented him, Kudu tossed his head—straight into a tree trunk. The other animals had to twist and turn him, curling his horns before they popped out. Zebra laughed again and resumed his slow munch towards Creator. He arrived as Yak was shaking his coat of long, warm hair.

Illustrated by Christopher Cooley

"Goodbye, and good luck on your journey to the cold country," called Creator.

"Zebra!" greeted Creator. "I know you feel a bit put out since you were created last. But I have made your coat like no other. It is white on one side and black on the other. You can change what color you are!"

Zebra was delighted. He chose to be white first. Creator pulled the coat over Zebra and smoothed it into place. Zebra sucked in his breath for he had grown bigger, eating all that grass! Creator grunted as he pulled the edges together and sewed them tight. As Creator took the last stitch, Zebra could hold his breath no longer. He let out a giant sigh, and the beautiful white coat split into stripes, showing his black coat underneath. And that is how it has been ever since.

— Cindy Blobaum

Ask Yourself a Question

When you ask yourself a question,
You have only just begun.
It's the search to find the answer
That makes asking so much fun!

Can a turtle feel a tickle
From a feather on its shell?
If a planet moved a mile,
Could a person even tell?

Why do magnets stick together?
Where does outer space begin?
Do you really need a mirror
If your brother is your twin?

Where's the bottom of a bubble?
Does a circle have an end?
Is it possible for people
To have more than one best friend?

If you plant a row of birdseed,
Will you grow a crop of birds?
Who decided how the letters
Go together to make words?

What if every single person
In the world looked just the same?
How does wind know where to go,
And how did pickles get their name?

Are the sunsets made of sherbet?
Where does peanut butter grow?
When you take your medicine,
How does it know where it should go?

What if babies grew on bushes?
Who invented knock-knock jokes?
Why do chickens come in colors
When all eggs have yellow yolks?

When you search to find an answer,
You will see your knowledge grow.
So go ask yourself a question,
And keep asking till you know.

—Susie Sawyer

Illustrated by Ben Vincent

Illustrated by Steve Young

THE BOX

I found a box outside one day, while looking for something to do.
So I climbed inside and started to play. (I'm sure you would've too.)

I poked my head outside the box, to see I was in space!
Oh, wow! I was an astronaut! So, I looked for aliens to race.

An asteroid knocked my shuttle aside, and I let out a disheveled grunt.
I was then a pirate taking a ride to begin a treasure hunt.

The wild waves pushed my ship back, and I peered around to see
I was a jungle explorer, in fact, camping on safari.

A rhinoceros slammed into my tent, and I fell onto a horse.
As a cowboy, I rode unbent, keeping my cattle on course.

But when a wild stampede befell, I found a helmet on my head.
A medieval soldier is quite swell, for battling dragons of dread!

Up the stairs and down the hall, I rode my noble steed.
After a day of having a ball—it was a wonderful box indeed!

I dismounted, thankful I had survived,
brushed my teeth with neither protest nor fight
And climbed into bed as my mother arrived.
She tucked me in and said, "Good Knight."

— Brooke Cummings

31

Ladybug

Ladybug, ladybug, where do you go?
Fluttering here and there, to and fro.
Ladybug, ladybug, happy as can be,
Flying over the flowers, landing on a tree.
Fluttering among the daisies as if all is well,
Stopping on a poppy to rest a spell.
Ladybug, ladybug, in what a lovely place you dwell,
Amid the violets, peonies and the pretty bluebells.
Ladybug, ladybug, open your wings and fly,
Fly to your home for darkness is nigh.
Red and black, black and yellow,
Landing on a sweet pea, resting nice and mellow.
Ladybug, ladybug, safe and snug.
Ladybug, ladybug, such a cute little beetle bug.

—Apryl Harris

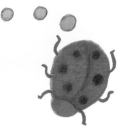

Illustrated by Kimberly Price

Walking the Dog

I heard the rain.
I saw the fog.
I did not want to walk the dog.
I'd rather read my morning paper
And plan to walk that black dog later.

But there she stood
Beneath her leash,
That hung just beyond her reach.
She looked at me. I looked away.
We'd have our walk later that day.

She ran to me.
She nudged my leg.
She looked at me as if to beg.

I felt the rain.
I joined the fog.
I went outside and walked that dog.

—Julie Potluri

Grandpa's Favorite Place

"Put on your shoes," Grandpa said. "We're going for a walk."

"Where are we going?" asked Mollie.

"To my favorite place," answered Grandpa.

Mollie put on her shoes and Grandpa tied them. Grandpa and Mollie walked across the garden. Mollie stopped to smell the tulips. Grandpa smelled the daffodils. "Mmmm," they said together.

"Is this your favorite place?" asked Mollie.

"No," said Grandpa. "I like the garden, but it is not my favorite place."

Grandpa and Mollie stopped by Uncle Bill's house. Uncle Bill was sitting on his front porch. Uncle Bill gave Mollie some puzzles to put together while he talked to Grandpa. "Is this your favorite place?" asked Mollie.

"No," said Grandpa, "I like to visit Uncle Bill, but it is not my favorite place."

Grandpa and Mollie climbed the steps to the library. "Let's read some books," said Grandpa.

Grandpa read a book to Mollie and Mollie read a book to Grandpa. "Is this your favorite place?" asked Mollie.

"No," said Grandpa. "I like the library, but it is not my favorite place."

Grandpa and Mollie crossed the street to the ice cream store. Mollie ate a chocolate ice cream cone and Grandpa had a vanilla one. "Is this your favorite place?" asked Mollie.

"No," said Grandpa. "I like the ice cream store, but it is not my favorite place."

Grandpa and Mollie turned down the alley. Grandpa clapped as Mollie danced in the puddles. "Is this your favorite place?" asked Mollie.

"No," said Grandpa. "I like the puddles in the alley, but it is not my favorite place."

Finally, they walked back down Mollie's street. "Now, we are home again," said Mollie sadly. "And we didn't find your favorite place."

"Yes, we did," said Grandpa. "Home again with you is my favorite place."

—Ellen Emerman

It Didn't Stop There

The pretty blue yarn was wrapped around and around the coffee table leg. Sadie found the end and unwrapped it. But it didn't stop there.

It went behind the TV and around the potted plant. Sadie rolled that up too, but it didn't stop there.

It went down the hall and outside. Then, it went around the tree and in and out of the bushes. Sadie rolled it into a ball of yarn. But it didn't stop there.

The pretty blue yarn went back inside and down the hall. But it didn't stop there.

From the hall it went into the bathroom, around the bottom of the sink and then into the kitchen. Sadie had to crawl under the table to get it all untangled from the chair legs. But it didn't stop there.

It went up on the countertops, into the sink and then up into the cabinets! There was a big pile on top of the plates, but it didn't stop there.

Sadie's ball of yarn was growing. The pretty blue yarn dropped back onto the floor and went back down the hall and into the den. It was tangled around the ironing board and then went up on the desk. Sadie rolled up another small pile from behind the computer, but it didn't stop there. No, siree.

It went into her bedroom and under the bed. It came out on the other side of the bed. The ball in Sadie's hands was very big, but it didn't stop there.

It went into her closet, and was tangled among her clothes.

And there…it stopped, in the closet, behind her clothes, on the floor. There Sadie found her new kitten, Whiskers, all curled up and sleeping on all that remained of her favorite blue sweater.

— Bridgid Janak

Sleepyhead

My little brother Phineas
Is such a sleepyhead.
He falls asleep at the table
Before he's even fed.

His eyes start to close.
His head starts to droop.
Before I can shout, "Phineas!"
He's asleep in his soup.

My brother Phineas
Takes catnaps all day,
When he's watching TV,
Or he goes out to play.

His eyes start to blink.
His head starts to sway.
Before I can shout, "Phineas!"
He's snoozing away.

Poor little Phineas
Just can't stay awake.
He sleeps in the car
No matter what road we take.

Z,ZZZZZZZZ

Illustrated by Mary Taylor

He stretches and yawns.
And you know the rest
Before I can shout, "Phineas!"
His head's on his chest.

But when Mom puts
Phineas Justin to bed
His big eyes pop open
And Phineas says,

"I'm hungry. I'm thirsty.
I need my bear.
Check under my bed.
There's a monster down there.

"I'm coughing. I'm cold
No, I think I'm too hot.
Do you wanna see
All these itchies I've got?

"I need to go potty.
Please turn down my light.
Why is my bedtime
So early at night?"

My brother Phineas
Is such a sleepyhead.
He can sleep anywhere—
Except in his bed.

— Jeanie Stewart

41

Little Green Tree Frogs

My gosh, look what I found! There's a frog in our sink!
How did he get there? What do you think?
It's always a mystery. It happens each year.
Whenever it rains, they all come in here.

Little green tree frogs hop under the door.
They jump and they jump across the slate floor.
They come by themselves. They come in big bunches.
Where do they come from? Here's what my hunch is.

These frogs live in the grass under our trees.
Then all the leaves fall and fly away with the breeze.
The grass withers up. There's nowhere to hide.
So all of the froggies come jumping inside.

They know it is warm here with water to drink.
So that's why the tree frogs jump into the sink.
They think its a great place and like it in here.
These frogs want to stay until spring comes next year.

— Pamela B. Harold

Illustrated by Natalie Russo

43

Achoo in the Deep Blue

All was quiet, as quiet as can be,
Down in the deep, deep blue sea.
Then one little seahorse started to sneeze.
He huffed and he puffed and he started to wheeze.
"Achoo," said the seahorse. "Achoo, ACHOO!"
He turned to the clownfish and said, "I can sneeze louder than you."
"Not true," cried the clownfish. "I can sneeze quite loud."
Then he did, with a smile that was quite proud.
"Achoo," said the clownfish. "Achoo, ACHOO!"
He turned to the jellyfish and said, "I can sneeze louder than you."
"Not true," cried the jellyfish, turning bright pink.
"I can sneeze louder than either of you think."
"Achoo," said the jellyfish. "Achoo, ACHOO!"
He turned to the stingray and said, "I can sneeze louder than you."
"Not true," cried the stingray, her tail starting to sway.
"I can sneeze louder than you have today."
"Achoo," said the stingray. "Achoo, ACHOO!"
He turned to the dolphin and said, "I can sneeze louder than you."

"Not true," cried the dolphin, squealing with glee.
"Nobody can sneeze louder than me."
"Achoo," said the dolphin. "Achoo, ACHOO!"
 He turned to the whale and said, "I can sneeze louder than you."
"I don't care," said the whale. "I've heard enough.
 All this arguing about silly stuff!
 If you want to hear a sneeze that is louder than all of you,
 Stand back. ACH-ACH-AAA-ACHOO!!!"
 The dolphin giggled, the ray started to sway.
 The bright pink jellyfish began floating away.
"Well," said the clownfish, "I must say,
 That was the loudest sneeze I've heard today."
 The whale just smiled and said with a grin,
"If you would like to be friends, I'll show you where to begin."
 All the sea animals shouted, "We would, of course!"
"Hiccup!" said the little seahorse.

—Elizabeth Vose

AUTHORS

Carmella Van Vleet	Missing the Big Parade	Lewis Center, OH
Amy Nichols	Harvey and the Horrible Sneeze	Peoria, AZ
Margaret King	Frequent Flyer	Indianapolis, IN
Janna Matthies	Snowflakes in the Night	Indianapolis, IN
Savannah Lyons	When I Grow Up	Columbus, OH
Donna Lee Murphy	Grandpa Pete and Me	Madison, WI
Cynthia M. Peebles	Seasons of Fun	Louisville, KY
Jessica Van Roekel	The Adventures of a Housecat	Corpus Christi, TX
Alex Rudd	My Adventures	North Bend, WA
Katie Beckman	Isabelle Winkle Touches the Moon (3rd Place)	Des Moines, IA
Cindy Blobaum	Animal Coat Catastrophe	Des Moines, IA
Susie Sawyer	Ask Yourself a Question (1st Place)	Rhinelander, WI
Brooke Cummings	The Box	Austin, TX
Apryl Harris	Ladybug	San Antonio, TX
Julie Potluri	Walking the Dog	Cincinnati, OH
Ellen Emerman	Grandpa's Favorite Place	Chicago, IL
Bridgid Janak	It Didn't Stop There	Trophy Club, TX
Jeanie Stewart	Sleepy Head (2nd Place)	Hayti, MO
Pamela B. Harold	Little Green Tree Frogs	Edmonds, WA
Elizabeth Vose	Achoo! In the Deep Blue	Duncanville, TX

ILLUSTRATORS

Alik Arzoumanian	Dena Bach Elovitz	Roman Koellerq	Ingrid Sundberg
Katie Beckman	Chris Goodwin	Julie Lyon	Mary Taylor
Dave Condry	Aleks Hadden	Halley Palmer	Erla Shehu
Christopher Cooley	Veronica Hebard	Kimberly Price	Ben Vincent
Ryan Cross	Patt Kelley	Natalie Russo	Steve Young

ABOUT THE COVER ARTIST

Chet Phillips began his career as a freelance illustrator in the early 80's. He has created work for advertising agencies, design firms, book, newspaper and magazine publishers and corporations. Trained in traditional media with a Bachelor of Fine Arts in Painting and Drawing, Chet made the transition to digital media in 1992. His "Digital Scratch Board" is created with the natural media software Painter. He lives in Dallas, Texas with wife Julie and two tabby cats Brodie and Lily.

"Children become readers in the laps of their parents."

Emilie Bushwald

We hope you have enjoyed the 13th edition of "Say Good Night to Illiteracy," published and supported by Half Price Books. This year, we are donating the proceeds of the book to the National Center for Family Literacy. NCFL was founded in 1989 and is dedicated to life improvement for the nation's most disadvantaged children and parents. Through their tireless efforts, NCFL has trained more than 150,000 teachers and thousands of volunteers, and firmly believes that literacy and education are the cornerstones of our nation's well-being and the building blocks of our nation's future.

As the mother of school-age children, I admire and applaud the NFCL's commitment to literacy. Through their groundbreaking initiatives, more than one million families across the country have made both educational and economic gains.

To learn more about supporting literacy go to halfpricebooks.com and click on the Community page or visit famlit.org.

Sharon Anderson Wright

Sharon Anderson Wright
President/CEO
Half Price Books, Records, Magazines, Inc.